SUNDAY EXPRESS & DAILY EXPRESS
CARTOONS

Sixth Series

A DAILY EXPRESS PUBLICATION

03440

4/6

OSBERT LANCASTER—also a member of the Daily Express fraternity of cartoonists—combines literary and artistic talent in making his from-the-heart tribute to a fellow artist . . . .

GILES . . .

THE work of Giles, like that of all great artists, has many aspects. There is Giles the nature-lover whose cows have frequently, and almost always favourably, been compared to those of Cuyp. Giles the landscapist who lives in the Constable country and carries on the best traditions of Gainsborough in that painter's birthplace. There is Giles the recorder of intimate domestic interiors who combines the scrupulous fidelity of a Vermeer with the warm affection of a Chardin. Examples of his works in all these genres will be found in the present volume.

But of all the roles which the artist assumes my favourite remains Giles the child-lover. Has any artist ever caught the fragrant, elusive charm of early childhood with such unvarying success? Reynolds, perhaps, in "The Heavenly Choir." But then by confining himself solely to heads, Reynolds deliberately shirked the issue in a way of which Giles would be ashamed. All Giles's children have a full complement of limbs; indeed, occasionally, one is not quite certain that some of them have not exceeded their quota.

Kate Greenaway? Possibly, but there is in Giles's work a vein of charming fantasy which she, I think, never quite managed to achieve. Indeed, some people have been

. . . compared to those of Cuyp

Giles the landscapist . . .

. . . Gainsborough?

among the Classics?

When asked to complete his foreword with an appropriate illustration, Osbert Lancaster responded promptly. Using the back of his manuscript, he executed a few deft strokes and produced this remarkable impression of the Man He Had Written About.

heard to wish that the master would devote himself exclusively to child portraiture, and while I cannot approve of any limitation of his genius, I can appreciate their sentiments.

Nevertheless, so great is his energy, so protean his accomplishment, that I am confident that sooner or later not only will his usual output be steadily maintained, but we shall be privileged from time to time to see on the walls of Burlington House a new "Bubbles", a 20th Century "Cherry Ripe" above the familiar signature . . . . *Tees*

. . . domestic interiors

. . . charm of early childhood

"The Heavenly Choir"

. . . a new "Bubbles"!

The English

GILES presents a story to strike a chord in many hearts. You could call it "The Graduation of a Husband—from First Stirrings—to the Full Burden."

1. *Youth's call to youth*   2. *First damping of ardour*   3. *Nightly vigil at her window*   4. *First success*

9. *The parting*   10. *The passing years*   11. *The reunion*   12. *Second instalment*

Husband

5. *Second damping of ardour*

6. *Wishful thinking*

7. *Fact*

8. *First instalment*

13. *Her parents (third damping of ardour)*

14. *Third instalment*

15. *Ripeness is all*

Now Start Again At No. 1

Daily Express, Dec. 3rd, 1951

"Lay off, honey—ain't my fault an American beat Turpin."

Sunday Express, Sept. 16th, 1951

"Watch out if them Tories get in—they'll want all yer teeth, glasses, 'air and bottles of free jollop 'anded back."

Daily Express, Sept. 21st, 1951

"Whoever gets in I expect we shall still have 'I've-brought-you-some-flowers-Mr.-Jones-and-do-you-think-you-could-let-me-have-a-little-extra-bacon-this-week?'"

Sunday Express, Sept. 23rd, 1951

"As shop steward of this school, I warn you that if Churchill gets in he'll have us all making armaments for the bourgeois capitalists' war, which will be a change from plant-stands and trays, anyway."

Daily Express, Sept. 28th, 1951

"He was a keen little lad—a bit Leftish perhaps—said he wasn't *always* going to work for me. Been reading the papers a lot lately and this morning he disappeared. So did my oil and pumps."

Daily Express, Oct. 9th, 1951

"Stroking my bull and calling him 'a dear old horse' don't give me a lot of confidence in your knowledge of agriculture."

Daily Express, Oct. 11th, 1951

"It's that beastly Socialist next door—left his car engine running to spoil Mr. Eden's TV election speech."

Daily Express, Oct. 17th, 1951

"But, my dear sir, one distinct advantage that an old car has over a new one is that you can buy it."

Daily Express, Oct. 18th, 1951

"You and your 'Only-way-to-get-the-troops'-vote-is-to-get-right-out-there-with-'em'."

Sunday Express, Oct. 21st, 1951

"But, Vera, surely we're being a little premature burning the family ration books."

Daily Express, Oct. 27th, 1951

"That candidate who kissed baby last week must have lost his deposit—he just gave baby a whack with his umbrella."

Sunday Express, Oct. 28th, 1951

"My Dad says he could get a jolly good banger for a ha'penny under a Tory Government when he was a boy."

Daily Express, Oct. 30th, 1951

"And now, if the last boy to leave school yesterday, November the Fifth, will kindly step forward . . ."

Daily Express, Nov. 6th, 1951

"Before we start again, Gentlemen, there are one or two little arrears outstanding from 1945."

Daily Express, Nov. 8th, 1951

"Gathering winter fu-u-el. . . ."

Sunday Express, Nov. 11th, 1951

"You know what *I* think about newspapers that make secretaries spend their time filling in entries for 'Ideal Secretary' competitions."

Daily Express, Nov. 14th, 1951

"Father says providing he ain't called up, sold up, or blown up, he'll be delighted to be Santa Claus at the kiddies' Christmas party."

Daily Express, Nov. 16th, 1951

"A few night-guard duties in Squire's woods'll help the meat ration—'Halt, who goes there?'
No answer. Bang! And down comes a pheasant."

Sunday Express, Nov. 18th, 1951

"To avoid unnecessary Inquiries I'll tell you now—it DON'T apply to you Regular soldiers."

Sunday Express, Nov. 25th, 1951

"Cease play, men. This ground must be fought for and won so that it can be handed
back to the enemy after the armistice."

Sunday Express, Dec. 2nd, 1951

"You will appreciate that your application to build next door to the chairman of the housing board will have a tendency to retard your priority claim."

Daily Express, Dec. 6th, 1951

"They might have told me they were going to build an A-bomb plant opposite *before* they let me buy my own house."

Sunday Express, Dec. 9th, 1951

"Fred, call Myrtle—I'm not having her running around with those dope addicts next door."

Daily Express, Dec. 11th, 1951

"We've abominable robins, abominable Santa Clauses at abominable prices—but no snowmen."

Daily Express, Dec. 13th, 1951

"Drunk in charge of a Zebra Crossing—that's what I am."

Sunday Express, Dec. 16th, 1951

"Emma! Get my slippers—I'll give 'em 'What am I doing wasting money on toys in times like these?'"

Sunday Express, Dec. 23rd, 1951

Life of

A Merry Christmas

the Party!

Daily Express, Dec. 24th, 1951

from GILES

"Wait till Dad hears you've had a dollar loan from those Americans who came for Christmas."

Daily Express, Dec. 28th, 1951

"All Mr. Churchill's efforts to maintain world peace mean nothing to some people's children."

Daily Express, Jan. 8th, 1952

"This 'let's-smell-your-breath!' campaign can scare every car off my new car park except that one—that's mine."

Daily Express, Jan. 16th, 1952

"You'd have thought Whitehall would have sent a few extra crates so we could wet the baby's head."

Daily Express, Jan. 18th, 1952

"I see somebody's mother isn't prepared to pay the Board of Trade's extra sixpence in the pound for laundry."

Sunday Express, Jan. 20th, 1952

"It's been reported that you went ski-ing instead of attending a football match on your day off."

Daily Express, Jan. 22nd, 1952

"You must explain to Fido in simple doggie language that he's not the only one who's disenchanted with our Government's meat policy."

Sunday Express, Jan. 27th, 1952

"If he's going to toss me two bob or nothing every time, there's not going to be much point in it."

Sunday Express, Feb. 3rd, 1952

"O.K., you just keep playing around out there—you'll soon see why it's better to stay indoors."

Daily Express, Feb. 19th, 1952

"Hey, Jack—would you mind explaining to your kids that we're opening an air base, not a candy store?"

Sunday Express, Feb. 24th, 1952

"Take your coat out of that puddle, Sir Walter Raleigh—here comes your mum."

Daily Express, Feb. 26th, 1952

"Reckon we'll be learning to walk agin after Budget Day."

Daily Express, Feb. 28th, 1952

"Bloomin' shame—can't afford two bus fares now, so the poor little wife has to walk."

Sunday Express, Mar. 2nd, 1952

"Many thanks. I now have a very legitimate excuse to pass the 'Needs Test' for a new car."

Daily Express, Mar. 5th, 1952

"The man in the pet shop told Vera that all his little birds would starve after Budget Day unless *somebody* bought them."

Daily Express, Mar. 7th, 1952

"Here's the Government spending millions of pounds on you—and you moaning
because I spend a few shillings on a new hat."

Sunday Express, Mar. 9th, 1952

"And only last night Dad was saying whatever the Budget result things couldn't get much worse."

Daily Express, Mar. 11th, 1952

"Extra child allowances only encourages 'em—damn phone's going day and night as it is."

Daily Express, Mar. 13th, 1952

"So we decided to borrow a page from history—form an outlaw band—rob the rich to feed the poor—and so on. . . ."

Sunday Express, Mar. 16th, 1952

Tendency of the British to shed pullovers at the first sign of Spring.

Daily Express, Mar. 18th, 1952

"One moment, my good man—his Lordship would like to know if you're going anywhere near Lincoln."

Sunday Express, Mar. 23rd, 1952

"All mine have gone to the Lincoln—what's your attendance like?"

Daily Express, Mar. 26th, 1952

THE CASH AND I

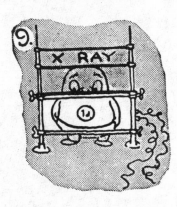 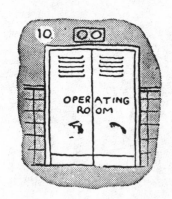  

MONEY: Like most people, I was born with none and had to acquire some before I could learn what life was like when it was gone.

Being always more interested in what you can get for it than in the stuff itself, I have never bothered to check up on how much I've got until the amount becomes so small it is very easy to see.

I had a useful indicator that it was time to be accumulating some wealth to provide the necessities of life.

My foot connected with a hot cigarette-end through a little hole in my sole, causing me to leap very high in the air.

I go all the way with Jack Hylton's remark that when he is working on a show there are so many problems seething through his mind that the money element really does not enter into it.

It seldom enters mine, and when it does it is always someone else who reminds me that it must sometimes be given consideration. Income-tax men are particularly allergic to this weakness of mine.

But if in the past, through lack of interest, I have appeared somewhat slow at paying out, it is to my credit that I am even more slow at gathering it in.

(*This doesn't mean that I have entirely forgotten one or two of you gentlemen in the pig business who haven't squared up lately. FINAL NOTICE.*)

If the love of money is not the root of *all* evil it is pretty nearly. For instance:

SAVE IT and collect a large bank account, and you're a miser.

BLOW IT as fast as you get it and they'll call you a waster.

IF YOU give it to charity, they'll say you're doing it to save

16. GO BACK TO Nº 6

tax. IF YOU don't, they'll say you're mean.

IF YOU die leaving a fortune, all except those who cash in on it will say you were a fool not to have enjoyed it while you were alive.

IF YOU did enjoy it while you were alive, what they'll say when you die leaving nothing couldn't be printed.

IF YOU spend your life buying friends drinks in pubs, you're a "drunk." IF YOU don't you're a "knocker."

Another thing: The more money you collect dishonestly or otherwise the more money you'll have to part with.

Up goes your salary and up goes the size of your car and up goes the size of your garage bills.

Get a bigger house and up go the number of week-end visitors and up goes the house-keeping.

Get a better job and higher go the standards you are expected to live up to, so up go the tailor's bills—until you get so rich that to go around with the behind out of your trousers is no longer a sign of poverty but of privilege.

Then one day in comes a Government which reduces the cost of living (just like it said it would before it was elected), and you're right back where you started—wearing that tattered old suit from necessity. But you won't be the only one.

So taking it all round, there doesn't seem to be any point in worrying about money, because . . . What's that you say, dear? . . . A message from the editor mentioning that after reading all this he has decided to do me a favour by knocking my salary in half?

Oh, I say . . . Look here. . . .

Daily Express, Mar. 22nd, 1952

"If it wasn't for people like Vera we wouldn't want a health service."

Daily Express, Mar. 29th, 1952

"Ain't that nice, Butch? You'll be able to tell the folks back home you nearly saw the Boat-race."

Sunday Express, Mar. 30th, 1952

"Good afternoon, gentlemen. We shall be paying particular attention to the little old expense returns up to and INCLUDING April the fifth."

Sunday Express, Apr. 6th, 1952

"You and your 'Let's sit under that hedge out of the wind'."

Daily Express, Apr. 7th, 1952

They're OFF!

A SOMEWHAT ECCENTRIC ALPHABET COMPILED

ASCOT

BOOKMAKERS

THE CESAREWITCH

DOPE

(See also PUNTER.)

EPSOM RACES

KINGS (SPORT OF)

THE LINCOLN

MUNNINGS

(See HORSES)

NEWMARKET RACES

THE OAKS

TIPSTER

UNSADDLING ENCLOSURE

VOGUE

FOR ALL FOLLOWERS OF HORSEY SPORT

by **GILES**

F Studying FORM argues that knowing what a horse has done in the past will give you an idea what he is going to do in the future. Anybody suffering from this illusion should take up horse-riding.

FORM

G

H

HORSES

Besides being used for racing they are also painted by Munnings.

I

ICE-CREAM MEN

If you want to make any money out of racing be an ice-cream man.

J

JOCKEYS

All jockeys look alike except Fred Archer, who didn't look like a jockey.

P

PUNTER

(Various)

Q

QUOITS

Quoits have nothing to do with racing, but they start with Q.

R

RAIN

S

SYSTEM (or The Scout)

(Take 200 horses . . .) Go ahead—count 'em.

W

See **BOOK-MAKERS**

WINNERS

X

EXERCISES

Horses talking.

Y

YARMOUTH RACES

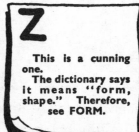

Z

This is a cunning one.

The dictionary says it means "form, shape." Therefore, see FORM.

ZOOMORPHIC

Daily Express, April 1st, 1952

Determination of the British to have their weddings at Easter.

Daily Express, Apr. 12th, 1952

"Nobody said anything to me about them coming through here."

Sunday Express, Apr. 13th, 1952

"So you're leaving us because our house is like a rabbit hutch? I did something taking you to see the Stately Homes this Easter, didn't I?"

Daily Express, Apr. 16th, 1952

"My dad reckons that anyone who has to spend all day with us ought to get the same as a Hollywood film star."

Daily Express, Apr. 18th, 1952

"Don't worry, son—when she reads how easy they're going to make it to get a divorce she'll change her mind and marry you after all."

Sunday Express, Apr. 20th, 1952

"In view of the fact that A-bombs are being televised in America, does the team think it would be possible to let one off during Children's Hour?"

Daily Express, Apr. 24th, 1952

"Boys, boys—not all of us think of May the first as Labour Day."

Daily Express, May 1st, 1952

"Honourable M.C.C. Gentlemen please to acquire consignment of cricket bats made in Japan very cheap?"

Sunday Express, May 4th, 1952

"Dad—we've found your Cup Final ticket we hid last week."

Daily Express, May 6th, 1952

"But Wilbur, maybe the little English boys don't want a little American boy to be admiral of their boats."

Sunday Express, May 11th, 1952

Owing to the fact that Towcester (neighbouring town to Silverstone) holds its Steeplechase meeting on the same day as the Daily Express holds its motor racing, visitors are advised to pay special attention to

the road signs marked TO THE RACES and the road signs marked TO THE RACES.

Daily Express, May 9th, 1952

"Germany rearming only a few miles across the sea isn't going to stop *me* having a paddle."

Daily Express, May 13th, 1952

"As commander-in-chief of the British Home Guard it sure makes me happy to tell you that your long-service medals are already being manufactured in Japan."

Daily Express, May 15th, 1952

"Pour another gallon on, Harvey—I'm not having Test Matches brought to me by somebody or other's little pills."

Sunday Express, May 18th, 1952

"Wilberforce informs me he is in love with teacher and therefore against the Teachers' Strike—we must remember to do Wilberforce after school."

Daily Express, May 22nd, 1952

"Careful, Herbert—Vicar isn't going to touch your mail bags."

"You and your witty remarks about the Guards being issued with smelling salts for Trooping the Colour."

Daily Express, May 30th, 1952

"But Paris Riots is not a *nice* game to play at a garden-party, is it, Ronnie?"

Sunday Express, June 1st, 1952

"Why—if it isn't that dear little man who wanted to see us home after the dance last night."

Daily Express, June 3rd, 1952

"He's all yours, m'Lady—getting over his last attack of B.R.M. nicely—but doctor says keep him off Test Matches for a while."

Daily Express, June 5th, 1952

"Let the Railways keep their turbot and powdered eggs at 7s. 6d. a time—that's what I say."

Sunday Express, June 8th, 1952

"Whoever is popularising polo can't know what we already have to put up with from football and cricket."

Daily Express, June 11th, 1952

"Well, I bet SPONSORED television would've had Gussie Moran AND Hopalong
Cassidy for the opening of Wimbledon."

Daily Express, June 13th, 1952

"Hold tight! Here's Geoff Duke right behind you—pull over to the kerb."

Sunday Express, June 15th, 1952

"Take it easy, Major, we've got them interested in the game—that's the thing."

Daily Express, June 20th, 1952

"Really, Martha, after a week at Ascot I should have thought we were entitled to a Sunday off."

Sunday Express, June 22nd, 1952

"Parm me, Bud—is this where we jump for the Little Mo show?"

Daily Express, June 26th, 1952

"Well, Willie was standing here yawning just as Stinker sent down one of his smashing forehand drives. . . ."

Sunday Express, June 29th, 1952

"Would it help if I was to report that I have never given a proper signal in my life?"

Daily Express, July 1st, 1952

"If you saw Fred's Missus you'd understand him being in love with his tram."

Sunday Express, July 6th, 1952

"There will be two minutes' silence while this delegation proceeds to the Peace
Council to sing 'Happy birthday to you'."

Daily Express, July 8th, 1952

"You'll notice your baby's been selling herself to the U.S. visitors again for a few sticks of gum."

Daily Express, July 10th, 1952

"There are *some* people who don't appreciate that there are *some* people who hate sport."

Sunday Express, July 13th, 1952

"I reckon they ought to send some of these go-slow strikers down here on a course."

Daily Express, July 15th, 1952

I must go down to the sea again, to the lonely sea and the sky . . .

Sunday Express, July 20th. 1952

Bold new satirist interprets classic English custom . . .

West End theatregoers are spreading the success of a satirist named Ian Carmichael in the new *Globe Revue*. Carmichael's act is simple—depends for its success mainly on the fact that nearly everyone at one time or another has faced the problem of undressing on the beach. For that's all Carmichael does—but here Giles comes in on the act too.

Sunday Express, July 20th, 1952

"But if we didn't call up your men for the Forces, how on earth could we afford to lend you soldiers to help with your harvest?"

Daily Express, July 23rd, 1952

"Next time they say: 'Little boys who cry will never make a soldier,' we'll say: 'What about Mossadeg?'"

Daily Express, July 25th, 1952

"Repeat after me: 'I, Ahmed Fuad, son of Farouk, do solemnly swear, NO DICE,
NO ROULETTE, NO LATE NIGHTS. . . .' "

Daily Express, July 29th, 1952

"Vera, go and tell our two Errol Flynns that we've found Grandma and the last bus
has been gone an hour."

Daily Express, Aug. 4th, 1952

"Dad says he hears the engineers may be going on strike, so he hopes you'll keep him waiting a long time for his mower repair."

Daily Express, Aug. 12th, 1952

"Quick! There's a brace of 'em—bottom corner by the window."

Sunday Express, Aug. 17th, 1952

This will make the Press unpopular—publishing pictures of Foxhunter watching Olympic athletes who hope to be the only men to win a gold medal at the International Horse Show.

Daily Express, Aug. 19th, 1952

"Edward! Put those papers away at once!"

Daily Express, Aug. 21st, 1952

"Don't forget to call on Auntie Maud in Plymouth—give my love to Cousin Gladys when you get to Cardiff—Uncle Archie won't like it if you don't look him up while you're in Blackpool—don't let Ronnie fall off, and remember the parcel for Aunt Kate in Glasgow, and when you get to Scarborough . . ."

Daily Express, Aug. 22nd, 1952

"Who gave me a lot of stuff about *I* was his only love—*I* was in his thoughts every minute of the day?"

Sunday Express, Aug. 24th, 1952

"Can we supply a set that runs on paraffin?"

Daily Express, Aug. 26th, 1952

"Just think, Mummy, when Spike and I are married, you'll be able to come and visit us in
New York two or three times a week."

Daily Express, Aug. 28th, 1952

"I read some interesting facts about education costing more than the police stations, fire stations, libraries, parks and highways all lumped together."

Daily Express, Sept. 1st, 1952

"If we sell all our best planes to America and they send 'em back to bases in England,
I reckon that's good business."

Daily Express, Sept. 4th, 1952

"What do you mean—you *bought* it?"

Sunday Express, Sept. 7th, 1952

"I'd cut girls right out of my life rather than go all round Britain on a —— bicycle to get 'em.

Daily Express, Sept. 8th, 1952

"And the next time we salute a German officer we'll do it without the 'Sieg Heil, Bighead' . . .
Most of 'em speak English."

Daily Express, Sept. 11th, 1952

"A little bird told the shop stewards that you have been telling people that a ban on overtime would mean long evenings washing up—doing the children's home-work and one thing and another. . . ."

Sunday Express, Sept. 14th, 1952

"We think your British Cotton Board is wonderful," replied a Japanese sweat-shirt manufacturer when asked what he thought of its arrangements for 20 Japanese cotton experts to visit a Lancashire Labour Exchange. They received a warm welcome and were presented with the usual bouquet by a little Lancashire lass wearing a cotton frock (our price 8s. 11d., Jap price 4¾d.), who later sang the Japanese cotton workers' anthem: "Half a pound of tuppenny rice. . . ." The Japs supplied the treacle.

Daily Express, Sept. 16th, 1952

"The 'enemy' is signalling that someone in our outfit isn't using blanks, sir."

Daily Express, Sept. 18th, 1952

"A very remarkable impersonation, Wilmot—now if you'll kindly put my hat back where you found it, and bring the cane over here . . ."

Daily Express, Sept. 23rd, 1952

"Daddy's a pet, really—but don't mention about America leaving the British out of the Pacific talks."

Sunday Express, Sept. 28th, 1952

"When tea comes off the ration next week I suppose we'll be losing old Hot-and-strong and Weak-and-milky."

Daily Express, Oct. 3rd, 1952

"These whites'd probably fine you ten bob if you let a firework off in Regent's Park."

Sunday Express, Oct. 5th, 1952

"This ought to be good—somebody said yesterday that the Welsh Guards are the smartest soldiers in Berlin. Them other four at the bar are Coldstreamers."

Daily Express, Oct. 7th, 1952

"There she goes agin—off to tell copper she've heard two more supersonic bangs."

Daily Express, Oct. 9th, 1952

"Here you see the girls gettin' ready for Lunnun on Tuesday."

Sunday Express, Oct. 19th, 1952